This

fimbles™

Annual 2005

belongs to

. . . .

There's something waiting to be found!

How many times can you spot this bucket in the pages of your annual? (Answer on p.63.)

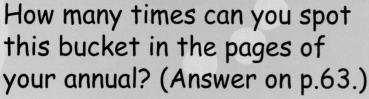

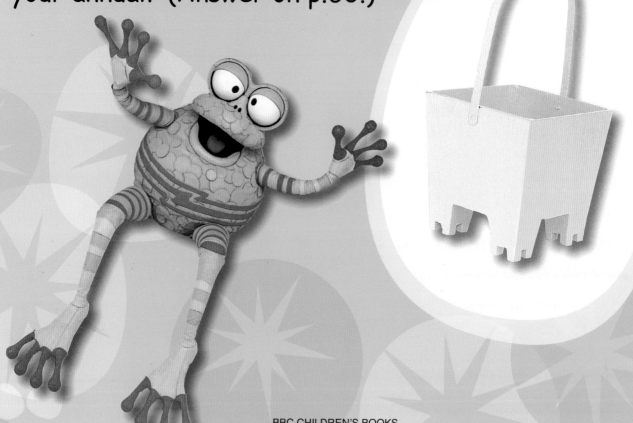

BBC CHILDREN'S BOOKS
Published by the Penguin Group
Penguin Books Ltd, 80 Strand, London WC2R 0RL, England
Penguin Putnam Inc., 375 Hudson Street, New York, New York 10014, USA
Penguin Books Australia Ltd, 250 Camberwell Road, Camberwell, Victoria 3124, Australia
Penguin Books Canada Ltd, 10 Alcorn Avenue, Toronto, Ontario, Canada M4V 3B2
Penguin Books India (P) Ltd, 11 Community Centre, Panchsheel Park, New Delhi 110 017, India
Penguin Books (NZ) Ltd, Cnr Rosedale and Airborne Roads, Albany, Auckland, New Zealand
Penguin Books (South Africa) (Pty) Ltd, PO Box 9, Parklands 2121, South Africa
Published by BBC Children's Books, 2004
Text, design and illustrations © BBC Children's Books, 2004
1 3 5 7 9 10 8 6 4 2
Written and adapted by Jenny Grinsted. Based on the television series scripts written by Alan Macdonald,
Catherine Kirkwood, Lucinda Whiteley and Toby Rushton, song lyrics written by Lucinda Whiteley,
Mike Watts and Lucy Murphy, and a short story written by Christine Secombe.
Design by Sue Newnham. Illustrations by Jenny Tulip and Bill Titcombe.
Photography on pp.24-25, 38-39 and 56-57 by Christopher Baines.
Photography on p.43 © Gillian Carlile/Alamy. Photography on p.50 © GettyImages/Chris Craymer.
Photography on p.51 © GettyImages/Ghislaine and Marie David de Lossy.
With thanks to Archie, Amelia and Anisha.
Fimbles © and ™ BBC 2002
BBC and logo © and ™ BBC 1996
CBeebies and logo ™ BBC. © BBC 2002

Fimbles is produced by Novel for BBC/BBC Worldwide Limited

"Hello chucks! Look what's inside your annual!"

What I Like to Do

Fimbo

"I like to Shimmy Shake,
That's what I like to do,
Shake, shake, shake!
You shake with me, too!"

Rockit

"Glung! I like bouncing round the valley,
That's what I like to do,
And I like jokes, songs and surprises...
There's lots of things I like to do!"

"Pom like pushing Trundle Truck!
That's what Pom like to do,
And Pom like story,
You can listen too!"

Pom

Roly Mo

"Ho hum, let's see...
I like books, old and new,
Reading stories, rhymes and poems,
That's what I like to do!"

7

"I like to draw and paint,
In red and yellow and blue,
Painting stars and flowers,
That's what I like to do!"

Florrie

Bessie

"I like to fly, chickadees,
That's what I like to do,
And see the big wide world,
Perhaps one day I'll see you!"

Ribble

"Cheep cheep cheep
cheep cheep!"

8

"And we really, really,
really like to play!"

Scrapbook

Florrie was drawing in the Busy Base.

"What can I draw?" she wondered. "I know, a star!"

"What are you doing, Florrie?" asked Fimbo.

"Drawing," said Florrie. "Look, I've drawn a star picture for you. Now, what else can I draw? I know! I'll go and draw my Giggling Garden."

"Reading stories, rhymes and poems, that's what I like to do!"

Fimbo went to look for somewhere to keep his star picture.
He wished he had something to give Florrie in return.
Suddenly, his fingers started to twinkle...

"I'm getting the Fimbling
Feeling!" he cried.
Fimbo found a big,
colourful book, but
when he opened
it... there was
nothing inside.
"Pom, Rockit,
Bessie, look what
I've found!"
he called.

"Tippity toppity! A book! Is there a story in it?" asked Rockit.

"It's empty!" said Fimbo.

Bessie laughed. "This is a scrapbook, Fimbo. It's for sticking your best things in."

"I'm going to fill it with Florrie's best things, and give it to her," said Fimbo. "And I'm going to start with this star picture, because Florrie loves drawing."

"Florrie best things!" shouted Baby Pom.

"Shhhh!" said Fimbo. "Let's make the book a surprise."

Fimbo, Baby Pom and Rockit went to find out what Florrie's best things were. Fimbo and Baby Pom found Florrie in the Giggling Garden.

"The Giggling Garden is one of your best things, isn't it, Florrie?" Fimbo asked.

"Oh yes!" said Florrie. "But the flowers won't stay still! They're too difficult to draw. I'm going to go and ask Roly Mo to tell me a story instead."

"We can't put a garden in a scrapbook," said Fimbo, when Florrie had gone.

"Pom know," said Baby Pom. She reached out to one of the flowers. "Petal please, flower?"

A petal fell off.

"Thank you, flower," said Baby Pom.

"Let's go and stick it in the book!" said Fimbo.

Rockit found Florrie with Roly Mo and Little One.

"Oh Rockit!" said Florrie. "Roly told me a lovely story about a big cactus and a little cactus in the sandy desert. Stories are one of my best things!"

"Glung! Stories!" said Rockit.
"Did you say stories? Hee hee!"
Fimbo and Baby Pom had stuck
the star picture and the petal into
Florrie's scrapbook.

"Hmm, we need something else..."
said Fimbo, as Rockit bounced up.

"Glung! Sand!" shouted Rockit.
"One of Florrie's best things is
stories. Roly just told Florrie a
story about a sandy desert.
So sand will remind her of
the story!"

Fimbo put glue on a page in the
scrapbook, and sprinkled sand from
the Funpuddle onto the page.

"Florrie's coming!" said Rockit.

"What's that you've got, Fimbo?" asked Florrie.

"A present for you," said Fimbo. "It's a scrapbook with all your best things in it."

"My star picture!" said Florrie, opening the book. "And a petal from my Giggling Garden! What's this? Sand? Oh, like the sand in Roly's story! Thank you! I love it. But... there's something missing."

"What that?" asked Baby Pom.

"My best thing of all," said Florrie. "My friends."

"Can you help us, Tinkling Tree?" asked Fimbo.

Florrie's scrapbook began to sparkle...

"Look!" said Florrie.

On one of the blank pages of the scrapbook, a picture of the Fimbles had appeared.

"Thank you, everyone! Thank you, Tinkling Tree!" said Florrie. "It's the best present ever!"

The End

Finish Florrie's Scrapbook

Can you help finish off these pages from Florrie's scrapbook?

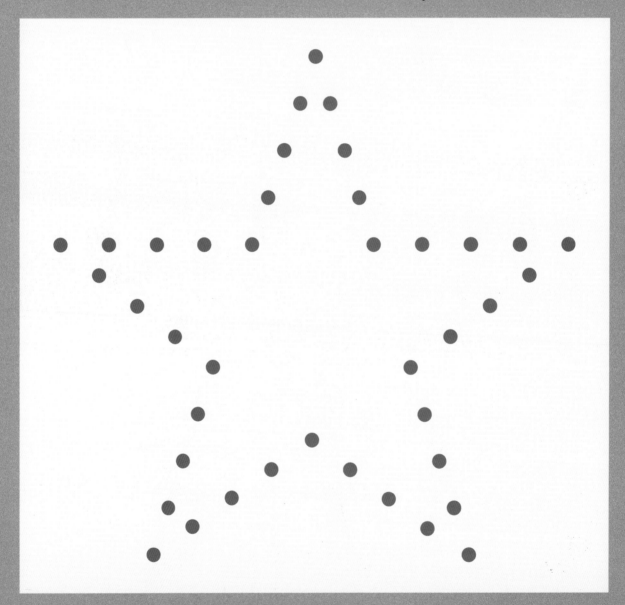

Join the dots to finish Florrie's star picture.

Colour in the picture
of the Fimbles.

Make Your Own!

Now it's time to make your own miniature scrapbook!

Cut out the page opposite and follow the step-by-step instructions to make your scrapbook. Then fill in the gaps and draw or stick something on each page that reminds you of your favourite food, animal, shape, game and flower.

You will need round-ended scissors and a 22cm piece of ribbon, string or wool.

Ask a grown-up to help.

1
Cut along the red dotted lines.

2
Fold the little pages along the blue lines.

3
Using the page numbers to help you, put the pages together in the right order.

4
Cut along the yellow dashed lines, through all the pages, to make two holes in your book.

5
Open the book to the middle pages, thread the ribbon, string or wool through the holes, and tie the ends in a bow.

6
Fill in the gaps and draw or stick something on each page.

Inside this scrapbook
are lots of

_____'s

best things.

12

My Best
Things
Scrapbook

1

My favourite

flower

is a

_____.

10

3

My favourite

game

is

_____.

8

5

My favourite
food
is

_____.

2

11

My favourite
shape
is a

_____.

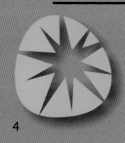

4

9

My favourite
animal
is a

_____.

6

7

Trundle Truck Spot-the-Difference

Spot four differences between these two pictures of Baby Pom and her Trundle Truck.

"Pom like pushing Trundle Truck!"

Answers: In the second picture, Baby Pom is holding an apple and her nose has turned blue, there is a flower in her Trundle Truck and it is missing a wheel.

21

BOING!

"I can't find Rockit anywhere! He's not in his tree. He's not with Florrie at the Busy Base. Roly Mo hasn't seen him, and Bessie and Pom haven't either!"

"Hee hee!
I like bouncing!
I'm hiding, and
I'm going to
bounce out and
surprise Fimbo!"

"Where could he be?
Have you seen him
anywhere?"

BOING!

PULL

Ask a grown-up to help
you fold this page along
the folding lines (------)
as shown. Then you can
play "BOING!" by pulling
the page outwards to
unfold it.

FOLD

FOLD

Shimmy Shaker Maker

You will need:
- a grown-up to help
- three paper cups
- seeds or rice
- sticky tape
- round-ended scissors
- an 8cm piece of wooden dowling (sanded so there are no splinters)
- orange and purple felt
- safe glue

1 Put some seeds or rice into one paper cup. Use sticky tape to stick a second cup on top of it, rim to rim. This is your shaker.

4 Glue one end of the dowling to the base of the third cup. Leave to dry. Put glue on the insides of the strips of paper and squeeze them round the dowling. Wind sticky tape around the outside to secure them.

2 Use sticky tape to stick the third cup to one end of the shaker, base to base. This will be your handle.

3 Cut from the rim of the third cup down to about 2cm from the base. Repeat this all around the cup, at 1cm intervals, to make strips of paper.

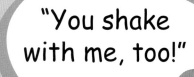

"You shake with me, too!"

5 Cut out and glue circles of purple felt over the top of the shaker and the end of the handle. Wind purple strips around the handle and glue in place. Glue purple and orange petal shapes all over the shaker.

Draw and Paint with Florrie

Can you finish this picture of Florrie's Giggling Garden? Dip your fingers into green fingerpaint, then press them onto the page to make lots of leaves. When you have finished, wash your hands.

"I like to draw and paint!"

Draw a picture of yourself with your favourite Fimble.

Flying Games

"I like to fly, chickadees!"

Bessie is trying to find Ribble.
Can you help her find the way?

Fimbly Bimbly Feeling

"Pom getting a Fimbly Bimbly Feeling!
We're going to find something new.

Hooray!

Feel a twinkling,
Hear a sound,
It's something
Waiting to be found!
Where is it? Where is it?
What could it be?
Something over there
Let's go and see!"

Turn the page to see
what Baby Pom finds...

29

Three Bowls

"Pom find big bowl, small bowl and bowl in between big and small!"

How many bowls are there?

What colour are they?

Which is the biggest?

Which is the smallest?

Which is medium-sized?

Ask a grown-up to help you find a bowl in your house. What does it feel like? Circle the words below you think describe it. Can you think of any more?

rough

light

cold

warm

heavy

smooth

Draw lines to join up the biggest bowl to the biggest Fimble, the medium-sized bowl to the medium-sized Fimble, and the smallest bowl to the smallest Fimble.

Are You All Sitting Comfortably?

Roly Mo is telling the Fimbles the story of Goldilocks and the Three Bears.

Goldilocks and the Three Bears

Once upon a time, there were three bears: Father Bear, Mother Bear and Baby Bear. Most of the time they were very happy. Sometimes, though, Baby Bear was sad because he had no one to play with.

One morning, Mother Bear made porridge for breakfast. But when the three bears tried to eat their breakfast out of their three bowls, the porridge was too hot to eat.

Father Bear said, "Let's go for a walk, and leave the porridge to cool down." So they did.

Somebody else was out for a walk that morning, too. It was Goldilocks.

When she came to the bears' house, Goldilocks saw the three bowls of porridge on the kitchen table.

"Ooh... I'm rather hungry!" said Goldilocks. She tried the first bowl of porridge. It was too hot.

The second bowl was too cold.

The third bowl was just right, so she ate it all up.

Then Goldilocks said, "Ooh... I'm rather tired!"

So she went upstairs and tried the first bed she found. It was too hard.

The second bed was too soft. The third bed was just right, and she fell fast asleep in it.

Soon the three bears came back from their walk.

Father Bear said, "Who's been eating my porridge?"

Mother Bear said, "Who's been eating my porridge?"

Baby Bear said, "Somebody's been eating my porridge and they've eaten it all up!"

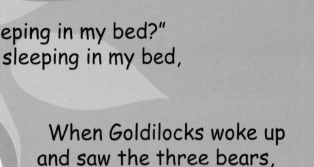

The three bears went upstairs.

Father Bear said, "Who's been sleeping in my bed?"

Mother Bear said, "Who's been sleeping in my bed?"

Baby Bear said, "Somebody's been sleeping in my bed, and she's still there!"

When Goldilocks woke up and saw the three bears, she was so surprised she ran straight down the stairs.

"Oh, do stay and play with me!" said Baby Bear.

So Goldilocks played with Baby Bear, and Mother Bear made delicious porridge for everyone!

The End

Goldilocks
Odd One Out

Which of these pictures of Goldilocks
is the odd one out? Colour it in.

1

2

3

4

Answer: Picture 3

Where are the Bears?

Goldilocks has come back to play again with Baby Bear, but she can't find her way through the woods. Which path takes her to the three bears' house?

Party Apple Flapjacks

Ingredients:
- a grown-up to help
- 250g butter
- 150g sugar
- 150g golden syrup
- pinch of salt
- 375g porridge oats
- 2 apples,
  cored and peeled

1 Grease a baking tin measuring about 20cm x 30cm.

4 Press the flapjack mixture into the baking tin. Ask a grown-up to bake it at 180°C for 25-30 minutes.

2 Put the butter, sugar, salt and golden syrup into a saucepan. Ask a grown-up to heat the mixture over a moderate heat, stirring until the butter has melted.

3 Ask a grown-up to grate the apples into a bowl and add the porridge oats and melted butter mixture. Stir.

"Next time you have a party, why don't you make these tasty apple flapjacks?"

5 Let the flapjacks cool down before asking a grown-up to help you cut them into squares. Now it's time for the party!

Three Fimble Bears!

The Fimbles are pretending to be the three bears.

Spot these things
in the picture.

green topknot	small green bowl	purple nose	four pink toes	two dark blue flowers

Goldirockit Jigsaw

And guess who's pretending to be Goldilocks?

Here's a two-in-one Goldirockit and the Three Fimble Bears jigsaw to cut out and play with.

Ask a grown-up to help you cut out the jigsaw below along the dotted lines. Then mix up the pieces and get puzzling! When you have finished one jigsaw puzzle, turn the pieces over, mix them up again and try the other puzzle.

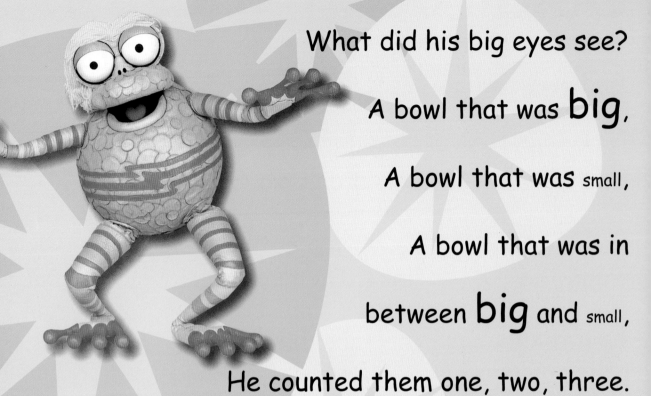

When Goldirockit came to the house of the bears,

What did his big eyes see?

A bowl that was **big**,

A bowl that was small,

A bowl that was in

between **big** and small,

He counted them one, two, three.

If I Were a Real Bear...

Brown bear

"Ooh, hello! Bears aren't only found in stories, you know. There are lots of different kinds of real bears, and they live all over the world."

"If I were a real bear, I'd sleep all winter!"

"If I were a real bear, I'd eat honey instead of apples and Crumble Crackers!"

What would you do if you were a real bear?

"If Pom real bear, Pom bear GROWWWWL!"

Comb

"Ribble!" called Bessie. "Where are you, my little fluff puff? Oh, there you are! It's time for your bath, little chook!"

Ribble cheeped loudly. He didn't like having baths!

"I know it's not your favourite thing, poppet," said Bessie, "but your feathers are all messy, and bubbles can be ever so much fun. Isn't that right, Fimbo?"

"Cheep cheep cheep!" said Ribble. He wanted to know if Fimbo really liked baths.

"Of course I like baths!" said Fimbo. "I love having my topknot washed, it feels all tingly and sparkly afterwards."

Ribble didn't believe Fimbo. And he really didn't want to have a bath.

"Where are you going, Ribble?" called Bessie, as he flew off.

Ribble found Florrie watering her Giggling Garden. "Oh, hello Ribble!" said Florrie. "Do you want to help me... ooh, did you hear that? The Tinkling Tree is telling me something!"

Then Florrie's fingers started to twinkle...
"It's the Fimbling Feeling!" she cried. "Can you see anything anywhere, Ribble?"

"Cheepity cheep!" called
Ribble. He'd found something
funny-looking in the
Comfy Corner.
   "You're right, Ribble,
it does look funny," said
Florrie. "It's hard and
it's got lots of straight
bits on it. I wonder what it
is? Let's go and ask Bessie."
   "Cheep!" cheeped Ribble, flying off
in the opposite direction. He knew that if Bessie saw him, he'd have
to have a bath.
   "Look what we found, Bessie!" said Florrie. "What is it?"
   Bessie laughed. "Well I never, you've found a comb! You pull a
comb through your hair, or fur, or feathers, to make them all neat
and tidy. It's called 'combing'."
                           "Oh, I wonder what I could
                              comb with my comb?"
                                said Florrie.
                                 "Well, once
                              Ribble's had his
                                bath, you could
                                use your comb
                                to tidy up his
                                 feathers,"
                                said Bessie.
                                 "He was just
                                 over there..."
                                said Florrie,
                              "but he's gone!
                              I wonder why?"
                              "I know why,"
                           laughed Bessie. "The
                           little sausage doesn't
                        want a bath."
      "Oh well, I'll see if I can persuade him!"
said Florrie. "See you later, Bessie!"

Ribble had found Baby Pom in the Playdips. "Cheep cheep cheep!"

"Do you not want to have your bath?" said Baby Pom. "Pom not like baths, either! Bubbles in Pom's ears and up her nose! Pom not like being clean!"

Then they heard Florrie looking for Ribble. "Where are you, Ribble? Roly, have you seen him anywhere?"

"Quick! Ribble hide!" said Baby Pom. "Pom hide, too!" They hid behind one of the trees.

"I can't find Ribble anywhere," said Florrie to Roly Mo. "And I wanted to comb his feathers and make them all neat and tidy with the comb I found."

"Cheep!" said Ribble. He liked the idea of having his feathers combed.

"Shhh, Ribble!" whispered Baby Pom.

"What was that?" said Roly Mo. "Ribble? Pom? Are you hiding?"

"Cheep cheep!" cheeped Ribble to Florrie, fluttering out of his hiding place.

"You want me to comb your feathers?" asked Florrie. "But Ribble, I can't comb your feathers until you've had a bath."

Ribble cheeped again. He thought that perhaps he was ready for his bath now.

"Well done, Ribble!" said Florrie.

When Ribble had finally had his bath, Florrie carefully combed his feathers. "There, isn't that better, Ribble?" she said.
"Ribble lovely. Ribble can see now!" said Baby Pom.
"Cheep cheep cheep!" cheeped Ribble. Perhaps baths weren't so bad after all.

The End

Baths and Bubbles

"Shall we have a look and see some other people having baths?"

This boy is having a bath. How many ducks are there in the picture?

What are these children playing with? Write over the dotty word.

bubbles

After you've had a bath, which of these things could you use a comb to comb?

your teeth   your nose   your toes   your hair

51

Bathtime Board Game

This game is for two to four players. You will need a counter for each player, and a die.

It's bathtime in Fimble Valley! Who will have their bath first?

Start

Start

Put your counters on the large Start flowers. Then take turns to throw the die and move your counters along the smaller flowers towards the Playdips. The player who reaches the Playdips first, with the right throw of the die, is the winner.

Start

Start

Rockit's Bathtime Rhyme

"Here's a special rhyme to say the next time you're having a bath. Glung!"

Rub a dub dub,
Scrubbidy scrub,
How many bubbles are
in my tub?

Come on everyone,
Let's splish and splosh,
There's nothing to beat
a really good wash.

Rub a dub my nose,
Scrub between my toes,
I'm going to smell as fresh
as a rose!

Come on everyone,
I think you know what I mean,
It feels so good when you're
squeaky clean!

Bubble Fall Collage

1 Mix the blue poster paint, water and washing-up liquid in the plastic container. Use the straw to blow into the mixture until you have a mound of blue bubbles.

2 Lower the white card onto the mound of bubbles until they pop and make blue bubble prints on the card. Repeat until most of the card is covered.

You will need:
- a grown-up to help
- 20ml washing-up liquid
- 60ml blue poster paint
- 40ml water
- shallow plastic container
- drinking straw
- stiff white card
- brown and orange sugar paper
- round-ended scissors
- safe glue
- old magazines
- glitter

3 Rip the sugar paper into pieces and stick them over parts of the bubble prints, to make the rocks at the sides of the Bubble Fall.

4 Cut out flower and leaf shapes from the old magazines, and use them to decorate the rocks.

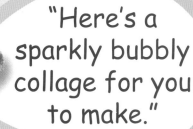

"Here's a sparkly bubbly collage for you to make."

5 Finally, dab some glue onto the blue bubble prints, then sprinkle glitter over it. Shake off the excess glitter and you'll have a beautiful sparkly Bubble Fall collage!

Busy Base Find and Colour

The Fimbles are making their own collage in the Busy Base. But somewhere in the picture, Ribble is hiding from Bessie.

Can you find him?

When you have found Ribble, finish colouring in the picture.

59

What a Busy Day!

"Well, we've certainly had a busy day today, haven't we? First of all found a .

, and found out what 's best things were and stuck them in the , then they gave the to . Wasn't that nice of them? found . We told the story of Goldilocks and the Three Bears, then , and pretended to be the Three Bears, and pretended to be Goldilocks! Little fell asleep in one of the bowls, and told everyone about real bears.

Fimbo

Florrie

Baby Pom

Bessie

Follow the code to help Roly Mo tell the story of what the Fimbles have found today.

Cheeky little just didn't want to have his bath, and kept hiding from . But when  found a , and said she'd comb 's feathers with her after he had had a bath, he agreed.

Then showed other people having baths, , , and had a race to the bath in the Playdips, and made up a bathtime rhyme."

Ribble

Rockit

scrapbook

three bowls

comb

Can You Remember?

Now see if you can answer Bessie's questions about what's happened in your annual.

"In the story 'Scrapbook', what did Roly Mo tell Florrie a story about?"

"How many bowls did Baby Pom find?"